D0349572

To my sisters – S.K.

For Toby and all the Jeremies – T.T.

Bloomsbury Publishing, London, Berlin and New York

First published in Great Britain in October 2010 by Bloomsbury Publishing Plc
36 Soho Square, London, W1D 3QY

A CIP catalogue record of this book is available from the British Library

ISBN 978 1 4088 0449 0

All papers used by Bloomsbury Publishing are natural, recyclable products
made from wood grown in well-managed forests. The manufacturing processes
conform to the environmental regulations of the country of origin.

Printed in Singapore

1 3 5 7 9 10 8 6 4 2

www.bloomsbury.com

the COMIC STRIP

Greatest Greek Myths

Sally Kindberg
and Tracey Turner

LONDON BERLIN NEW YORK

Contents

MURDER, REVENGE, MONSTERS, SHIPWRECKS, LARGE WOODEN HORSES ETC...

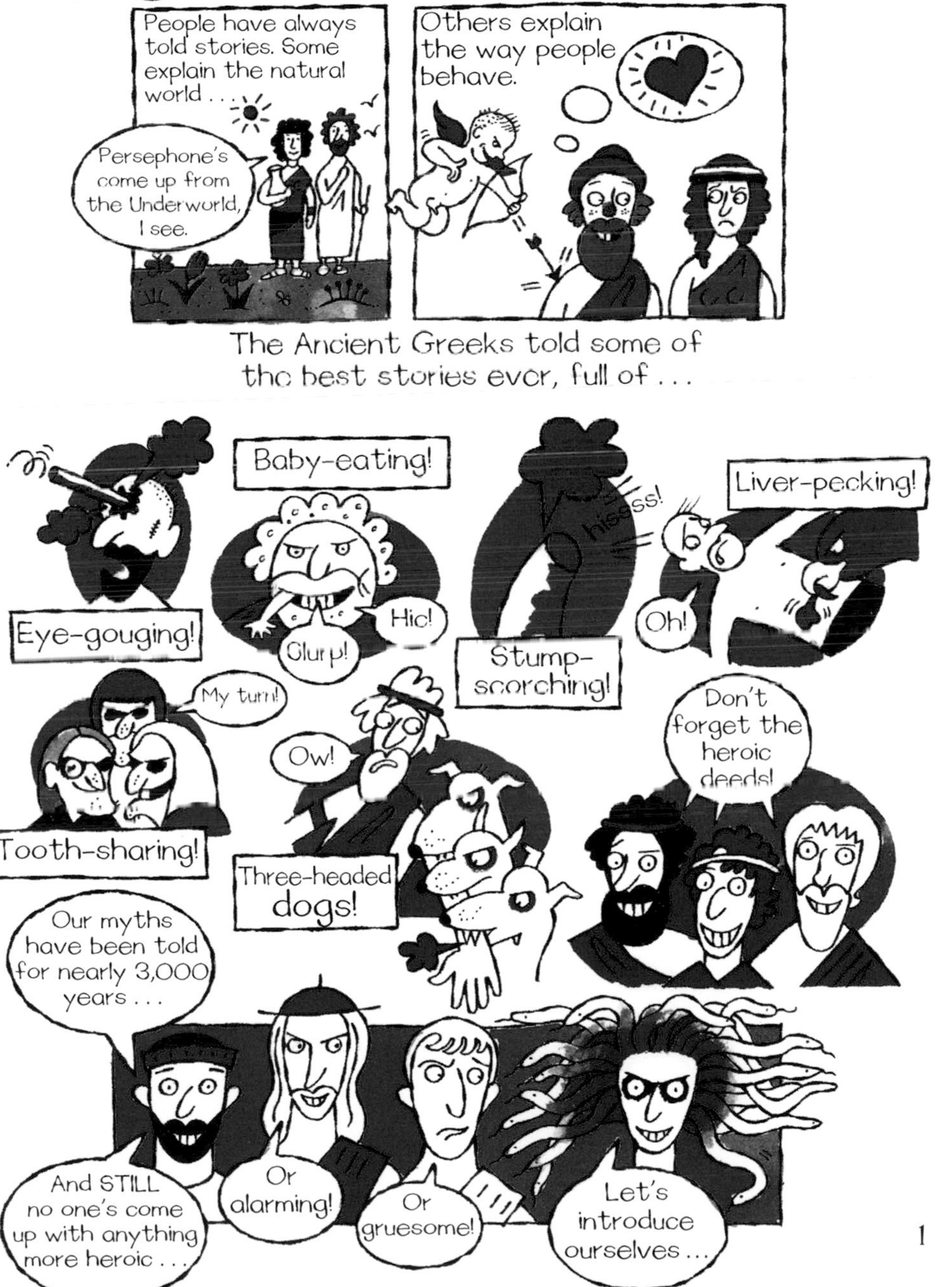

The Ancient Greeks told some of the best stories ever, full of . . .

Eye-gouging!

Baby-eating!

Hic!

Glurp!

hissss!

Stump-scorching!

Liver-pecking!

Oh!

My turn!

Tooth-sharing!

Ow!

Three-headed dogs!

Don't forget the heroic deeds!

Our myths have been told for nearly 3,000 years . . .

And STILL no one's come up with anything more heroic . . .

Or alarming!

Or gruesome!

Let's introduce ourselves . . .

MYTHICAL MONSTERS:

We're three ancient sisters. We share one eye and one tooth!

THE GRAEAE

GODS ETC.
A WHO'S WHO
I'm the top god, and these are my brothers and sisters.
We're called the Olympian gods, because we live on Mount Olympus.
ZEUS
Ouch!
I'm god of the sea.
POSEIDON
I'm the harvest goddess.
DEMETER
I'm the hunter goddess.
ARTEMIS
I'm god of wine.
Hic!
S'cuse me.
DIONYSUS
I'm god of the sun, archery and music.
Tum ti tum
APOLLO
I'm the warrior goddess of wisdom.
ATHENE

I'm Zeus's wife and queen of the gods.
HERA
I'm goddess of love and beauty.
APHRODITE
I'm Demeter's daughter and queen of the Underworld.
PERSEPHONE
I'm the blacksmith god of fire and volcanoes.
HEPHAESTOS
I'm the messenger god.
Must fly (ahem).
HERMES
I'm god of war.
Grr, gnash, etc.
ARES
I'm king of the Underworld. Heh heh!
HADES
I'm goddess of the home.
Cup of tea?
As well as us very important gods, there are minor gods . . .
and even some important human heroes . . .
HESTIA

WHO'S WHO (CONTINUED)
We're beautiful nature spirits.
Some of us are immortal . . .
Urk
NYMPHS
I'm god of goatherds and shepherds.
Toot toot!
PAN
We're goddesses of art, music, poetry and science.
There are nine of us.
THE MUSES
I'm goddess of strife.
Nng!
ERIS
I spin the thread of every human life . . .
I decide how long it is.
And I cut it!
Cackle!
Tee hee
THE FATES

I shoot arrows of love or indifference.
Depends on my mood.
EROS
We relentlessly pursue unpunished criminals.
Revenge!
Hnn!
THE FURIES
We're fierce warrior women.
Grr!
AMAZONS
I'm goddess of victory.
NIKE
We're mortal men, usually with a divine parent or two.
Strong!
Brave!
And modest!
HERACLES
THESEUS
ODYSSEUS
ACHILLES
JASON
PERSEUS
BELLEROPHON
THE HEROES
I'm one of the TITANS, an older race of gods, defeated by the Olympians . . .

IN THE BEGINNING...

CHAOS

Then there was . . .
the Earth
the Underworld

And a race of gods.
We're the Titans.
Some of us have baby Titans.
Not me, though.
Wah! wah!
Hnn
I'm Kronos.
clench clench

I EAT my babies in case they try to overthrow me - better safe than sorry!
Wah, wah!
Munch!

I'm Rhea, Kronos's wife.
I'm getting a bit fed up with this. I'm going to trick Kronos.

stone

He'll never notice the difference.

Here you are.

Yum!

Hic!

That one was a bit crunchy.

I'll call him Zeus.

Gurgle.

Years later . . .
Kronos had been right to be careful . . .

I'm Zeus.

Ha! You ate my brothers and sisters.

Nng!

Squeeze squeeze

Aarggh! I knew you didn't taste right!

I defeated the Titans, made Kronos regurgitate my brothers and sisters, moved to Mount Olympus and became ruler of everything!

Hnn

It's about time for a different myth – and this one's all about me . . .

PERSEPHONE QUEEN OF THE UNDERWORLD

We can't have this. Demeter, stop moping and change the season.
Sigh!
Right-o, Zeus.
Hermes, go and get Persephone from the Underworld.
Hnnn
No one who has eaten food here can ever leave the Underworld.
Here, have something to eat!
Heh heh heh!
Persephone ate some pomegranate seeds in the Underworld.
Ha! That means you can't return to the world of the living!
Tee hee
Aargh!
STAGGER STAGGER
Does that mean I've had a wasted journey?
As a compromise, from then on, Persephone spent nine months with her mother . . .
. . . And three months with Hades.
And while she's down there, it's winter up here.

Prometheus and the Theft of Fire

The Titans who had fought against Zeus were banished to the Underworld.

What a drag.

Yawn yawn.

I'm SO bored.

The others were allowed to stay.

Like me, Prometheus.

I'm still a bit miffed with Zeus, though, so I'm going to help out the weedy mortals for a bit.

Men! I demand a sacrifice.

An ox would be nice.

We'd better be nice to powerful Zeus!

Thanks. We gods will have all the lovely meaty bits . . .

and you lot can have the bones and yucky innards.

Eh?

Let's trick the old meanie!

gruesome bits

Yeah!

Eugh!

Prometheus and those puny men have tricked me! How can I get my revenge?

Oooh, I know!

Brrr.
It's so cold and dark.
Zeus has taken fire away from us.
Don't worry, men! I've stolen some fire from the god Hephaestos.
Here you are!
Right, that does it! Now I'm really cross.
As a punishment, Zeus had Prometheus chained to a rock. Every day an eagle came and pecked out his liver . . .
Oh dear!
. . . which would then grow back in time for the eagle's lunch the next day.
Yum!
Ouch
Not again!
TUG TUG
squelch
Don't worry – one day I'm saved by Heracles.
Now, how am I going to get my revenge on the men? Oooh, I know . . .

PANDORA'S BOX

I can't resist . . .
. . . I'm only human.
To P and E
Congratulations! Love, ZEUS XXX
DO NOT OPEN!

THE TWELVE LABOURS OF HERACLES

Labour 2: Kill the Lernaean Hydra.
Gaaa! Every time I chop off a head, two new ones grow back!
Aha! Burning the stumps stops them growing back!
Hisss
Phew! This one's immortal, so I have to bury it.
Labour 3: Capture the Ceryneian Hind.
Labour 4: Capture the Erymanthian Boar.

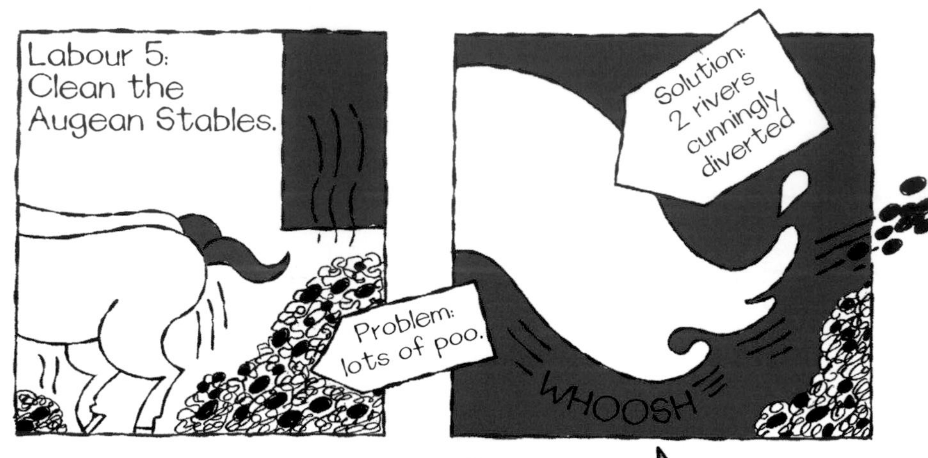
Labour 5:
Clean the Augean Stables.
Problem:
lots of poo.
Solution:
2 rivers cunningly diverted
WHOOSH

Labour 6:
Drive away the Stymphalian Birds.
CLACK
CLACK
Bronze castanets to scare birds from trees (a gift from Athene).

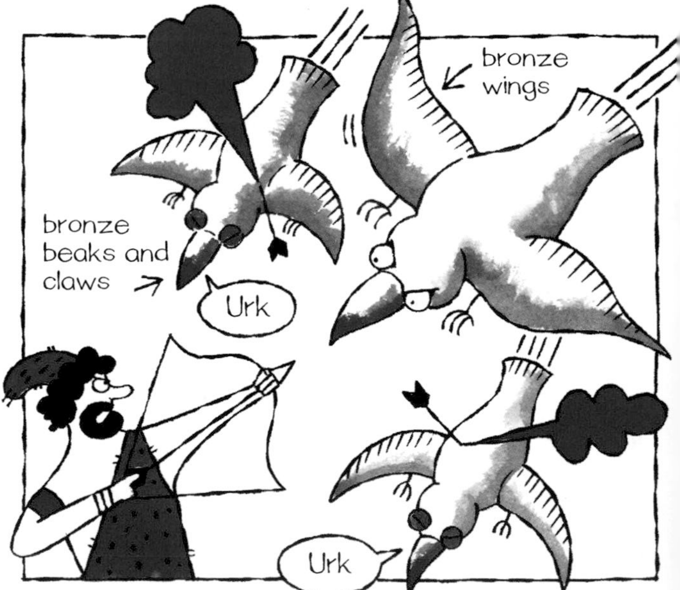
bronze wings
bronze beaks and claws
Urk
Urk

Labour 7: Capture the Cretan Bull.
Urk
Ha!
Labour 8: Steal the Mares of King Diomedes.
Killing the guards is the easy part . . .
Urk
Whinny
Gnash Gnash
Hmm, dinner!
It's the man-eating horses you have to watch out for . . .
Snort
Nnnn
I find they're much calmer after a good meal.
Muzzles to stop horses eating anyone on the way home.
Gee up!
Spoilsport!

Labour 9: Fetch the Girdle of the Queen of the Amazons.
Come on, Hippolyte, hand it over.
Get lost!
girdle

I tried asking nicely.
Heh heh
Urk

Labour 10: Capture the Cattle of Geryon.
Gah!
Hnnn.
Slaver
Moo
Snarl
That's Geryon. But I managed to kill him and his dog and nick his cattle!

Labour 11: Fetch the Apples of the Hesperides.
Hmm . . .
Zzz . . .

Atlas, if I kill the dragon, would you get the apples?
I'll hold up the heavens while you're gone.
All right, then.
I could do with a break and the Hesperides are my daughters.

Got them!
Labour 12: Bring Cerberus from the Underworld.
Fetching Hell's hound wasn't easy, I can tell you!
That's the last task – now I'm off to have a bath.
Yelp
Whimper
Growl

KING MIDAS AND THE GOLDEN TOUCH

How lovely!
gleam
gleam
Bother! I'll have to smell my roses without touching them.
Ping!
gleam
I feel a bit peckish. Oh no!
Hello, lovely daughter. Oh no!
Ping!
gleam
Dionysus! Please get me out of this mood!
Oh, all right, then. Go and bathe in the river Pactolus.
splish
splash
I hope this works!
From now on I'm not going to be so greedy. I might even share things a bit more!
Hooray!
Hooray!
Hooray!

KING MIDAS AND THE ASS'S EARS

What did you say, King Midas?
Gulp!
Oh, nothing, really. Just . . . you know . . .
There must be something wrong with your ears!
Oh no! I'll have to wear this cap to hide them!
Listen, barber, don't breathe a word of this - on pain of death!
I can't stand it any longer . . .
King Midas has ass's ears!
Later, reeds grew where the barber had dug the hole.
King Midas has ass's ears!
rustle rustle
King Midas has ass's ears!
Did you hear that? Quick! Let's spread the gossip!
I guess the secret's out. Now, where's that barber?
Chortle
Tee hee
Har har
Tee hee
Ho ho

JASON AND THE ARGONAUTS
My uncle, King Pelias, has promised me his kingdom of Iolcus if I can fetch the Golden Fleece from Colchis.
We're the Argonauts, here to help our pal, Jason.
Including me, the hero Heracles.
The Argo only just managed to get through these deadly crashing rocks.
whump
Then the Argonauts had to fight off the horrible, food-stealing Harpies.
Iolcus
AEGEAN SEA

And me, Orpheus, the famous lyre player.
And me, Atalanta, the only woman on board.
I've been made with magic speaking timber!
BLACK SEA
Colchis
Target: the Golden Fleece
Heracles cleared the land of giants at Cyzicus
Urk

When the Argonauts arrived at Colchis, the King of Colchis set Jason a task.
I'll give you the Golden Fleece if you plough and sow a field for me . . .
I bet there's a catch.
Of course, you'll have to use my bronze-footed, fire-breathing bulls, sow the field with dragon's teeth, and kill the warriors that sprout from them.
Gulp
I'm Medea, the king's daughter, and I can help . . .
Whisper whisper
I say!
Medea gave me a magic potion to protect me from the bulls' fiery breath!
Hnnn
Snort
Snort
Then she told me to throw a rock at the warriors to make them fight and kill each other. . .
. . . and it worked!
CLANG
Nnk!
Nnk!

The Golden Fleece was guarded by a fierce dragon. Medea gave the dragon a magic potion to make it sleep.
ZZZ
Let's scarper! I can claim the throne of Iolcus now.
And I'm coming with you, handsome.

But the Argo's journey back to Iolcus wasn't easy . . .
We were shipwrecked!
So we had to carry the Argo overland for a bit.
Phew!
Yoo hoo!
Otherwise they'd have eaten us!
Luckily, my playing was better than their singing and we escaped.
twang twang
Then we had to get away from the Sirens' song.
Nng
This is so typical!
Medea gave the giant a magic potion.
Zzz
Urk
And I worked out that taking out this nail will kill him!
Heh heh!

When Jason arrived in Iolcus . . .
Evil King Pelias killed my parents while I was gone!
What a rotter! Don't worry, Jason, I'll sort him out.
You're King Pelias's daughters, aren't you?
Would you like to help your father live for ever?
Oh yes, lovely!
If you chop up an old ram and put it in here . . .
Look! The ram is restored to a lamb!
Meh
They tried the same magic on Pelias . . .
Oh dear!
I wonder why?
Heh heh
It doesn't seem to have worked!
But there was no happy ending for Jason and Medea:
The trouble I went to, and this is the thanks I get!
Pah!
I abandoned her in the end.

SISYPHUS CHEATS DEATH

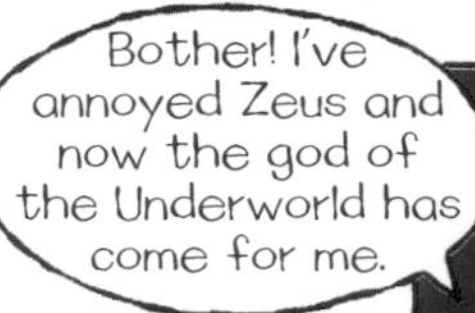

That's my husband dead, then. But something tells me he'll be back. He told me not to bury his body . . .

Hello, Merope!

I knew you'd be back!

Sisyphus lived happily to a ripe old age.

But now I'm ill and actually ready to die.

Bad luck. This time you're really for it. See that rock?

Sisyphus was condemned to roll a great rock to the top of a hill, only for it to roll back down again, for all eternity.

Urgh! This is SO boring!

Atalanta was left to die on a hillside . . .

Wah, wah . . .

. . . but was found by an unusual rescuer . . .

Hnn

Goo goo

After a start like that, it's no surprise that I've grown up as hard as nails!

And one thing's for sure: I'm not marrying some wimp!

Go on, I'm really nice!

Me!

Please, Atalanta!

No, me!

All right. I'll marry anyone who can beat me in a race . . .

Sounds fun.

What a stunner!

. . . and anyone who loses has to die!

Eek

Yikes

Gulp

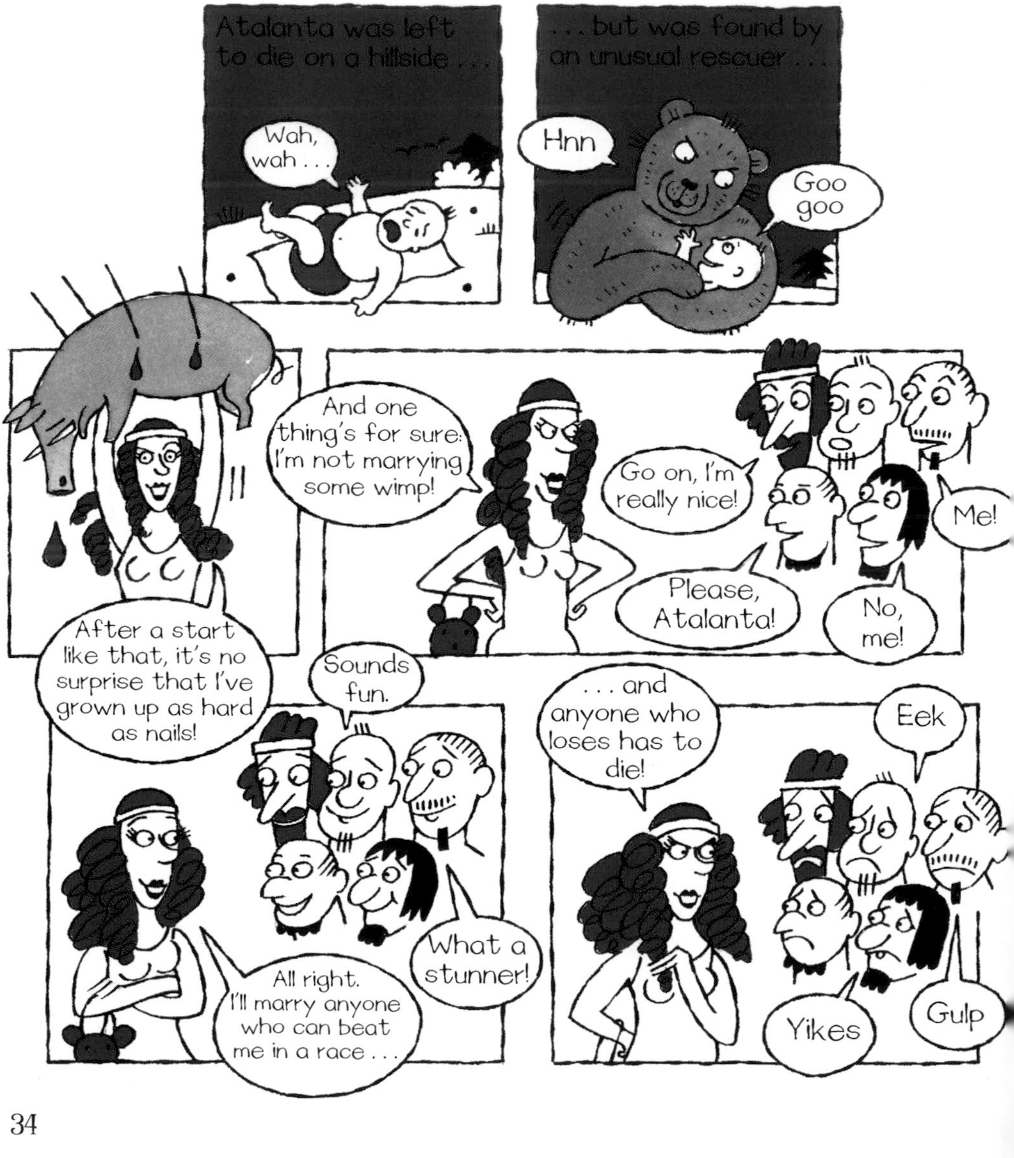

FINISH
Oh dear. Another one bites the dust.
Gasp, gasp
I feel like meddling in the world of mortals.
Oi, Hippomenes!
Good grief! It's the goddess of love, Aphrodite!
Take these golden apples to distract her, then you'll win the race.
Gosh!
Oooh, what's that?
You won, so let's get married - actually, I quite fancy you.
But Atalanta and Hippomenes didn't live happily ever after . . .
We offended Zeus.
Grr
So he turned us into lions.

THE LABOURS OF THESEUS

Serves you right, Sinis!
PING!
Hurrah for Theseus!
And now I'm just going to get rid of this monstrous sow -it's been terrorising the neighbourhood for years.
What a rotter!
Hnn
Nng
Hnn
Nng
I offer travellers either this short bed for the night or this long one. I just cut them or stretch them to fit!
Har har!
Not another evil-doer!
Gosh, I'm so heroic. Next stop, Athens!
Urk

King Aegeus's wife was Medea the sorceress.
Athens at last! Now all I have to do is find my father . . .
Hnn
I'm going to stop Theseus from telling his father who he is and ruining my own son's chances!
Husband! A deadly assassin has arrived to kill you!
Let's poison him!
Gosh!
You know best, dear.
We'll invite him to a feast . . .
Heh heh
THESEUS
Cheers.
STOP! Those sandals and that sword – it's my son!

Awww . . .
Dad!

And as for you, Medea, you evil, scheming witch, consider yourself banished!
Bother.

Snort,
Bellow
What's that?
Oh, that's the monstrous bull that keeps killing people.
Right!

Urgh!
He won't be bothering the people of Athens any more!

That reminds me, Theseus. Every nine years the people of Athens are forced to send seven boys and seven girls to King Minos of Crete, who feeds them to a bull-headed monster that lives in a maze.
Gulp!
Sort it out for us, would you?

Yikes
Erm . . .
this way?
Argh!
What was
that?

I want my mum!
MINOTAUR
Snort
BELLOW!
THESEUS
Anyone there?

Theseus was helped in his quest to kill the Minotaur by Ariadne, King Minos's daughter.
I'm in love!
Daedalus, you made the labyrinth, so you've got to help!
I'm sure Theseus can kill the Minotaur, but how will he get out of the labyrinth?
I'd love to help. I can't stand King Minos. He won't get out without this.
Take this special ball of wool - leave a trail and you'll find a way out.
Gosh, thanks.
You lot stay here. I'm off to kill the Minotaur. Back in a tick.

AARGH
AARGH
Ouch!
Urk
Thanks to Ariadne's ball of wool, we found our way out.
Hooray!
Come on, everyone! To the ships!

Bye!!

King Minos, Your Most Wonderful Highness, sire . . . I'm afraid the Minotaur is dead, and Theseus has got away and taken Ariadne with him!

Curses!

THE FLIGHT OF ICARUS

But Icarus DID fly too close to the sun. He crashed into the sea and drowned.

NARCISSUS AND ECHO

Poor Echo pined away, until only her voice remained.
Coo-ee!
Coo-ee!
Look, I know I'm gorgeous, but will you please just GO AWAY!
Gods! It's time that arrogant Narcissus was punished.
Help me, Artemis, hunter goddess!
All right. I'll make him fall in love with someone he can't have.
I say, who's that?
Narcissus had fallen in love with his own reflection.
Eventually he pined away, until only a beautiful flower remained in his place.

PERSEUS AND MEDUSA

We're the Graeae.
We only have one eye between us!
And one tooth!
Cackle cackle
We're not telling YOU where to find them!
Hello, Graeae. I'm looking for your sisters.
No way!
Never!
OK, no more Mr Nice Guy.
Straight up the road!
First left!
Nng!
Then right at the oak tree . . .

Hello.
Are you the Stygian nymphs?
At your service. You'll need this Cap of Invisibility.
That should come in handy.
And these Winged Sandals.
flip flap
I've always wanted a pair of those!
And this leather bag. It's to put Medusa's head in once you've chopped it off.
Thanks, nymphs!
flip flap
Wheee!

Ssss
Ssss
Ssss
Nnng
That wasn't so difficult after all. Mind you, I did have a bit of help.

Whinny!
I'm Pegasus and I sprang from Medusa's blood.
Snort

Meanwhile, after killing Medusa, Perseus was still feeling heroic . . .
What's that?
Help!

Andromeda was being sacrificed because her mother had boasted that they were fairer than the sea nymphs.
Fear not, beautiful woman!
Argh
Quick, get away while you still can! A sea monster's coming to eat me!

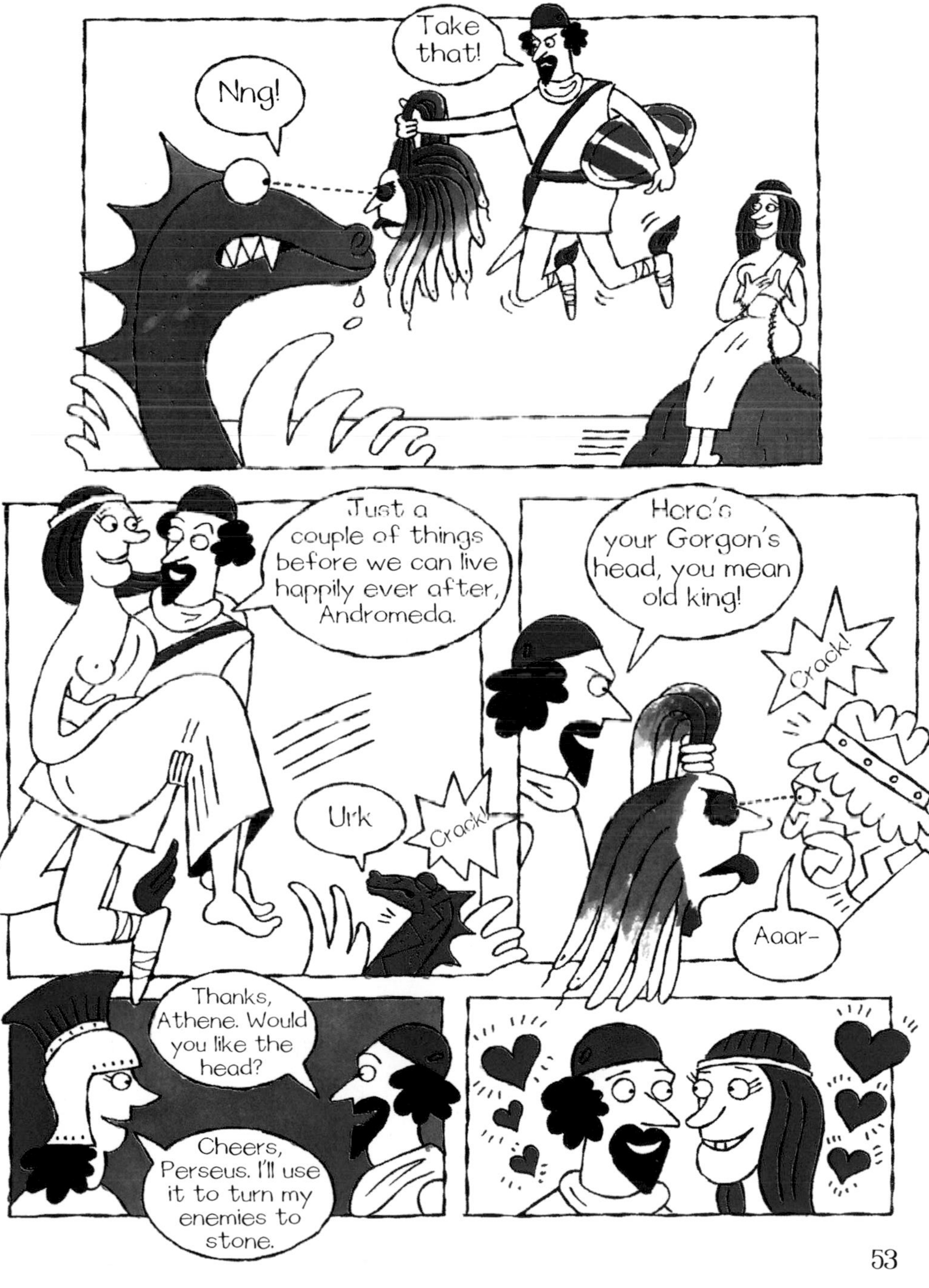

Just a couple of things before we can live happily ever after, Andromeda.

Urk

Crack!

Here's your Gorgon's head, you mean old king!

Crack!

Aaar-

Thanks, Athene. Would you like the head?

Cheers, Perseus. I'll use it to turn my enemies to stone.

BELLEROPHON AND THE FLYING HORSE

Bellerophon was given a task by the King of Lycia . . .

Bellerophon and Pegasus defeated the Chimera together . . .

ORPHEUS IN THE UNDERWORLD

This must be the River Styx. The dead have to cross it to get to the Underworld.
Will you take me across, ferryman?
Sorry, you're not dead.
Oh, all right then.
Your music has put me, Hades, ferocious god of the Underworld, in a good mood.
What can I do for you?
drool
yip
whimper
Hades, please let me take Eurydice back up to the land of the living.
Go on, then. But you mustn't look back till Eurydice is in the sunlight again, or she'll be lost for ever.
I might just have a peek.
You complete twit, Orpheus! Goodbye for ever!

KING TANTALUS'S PUNISHMENT

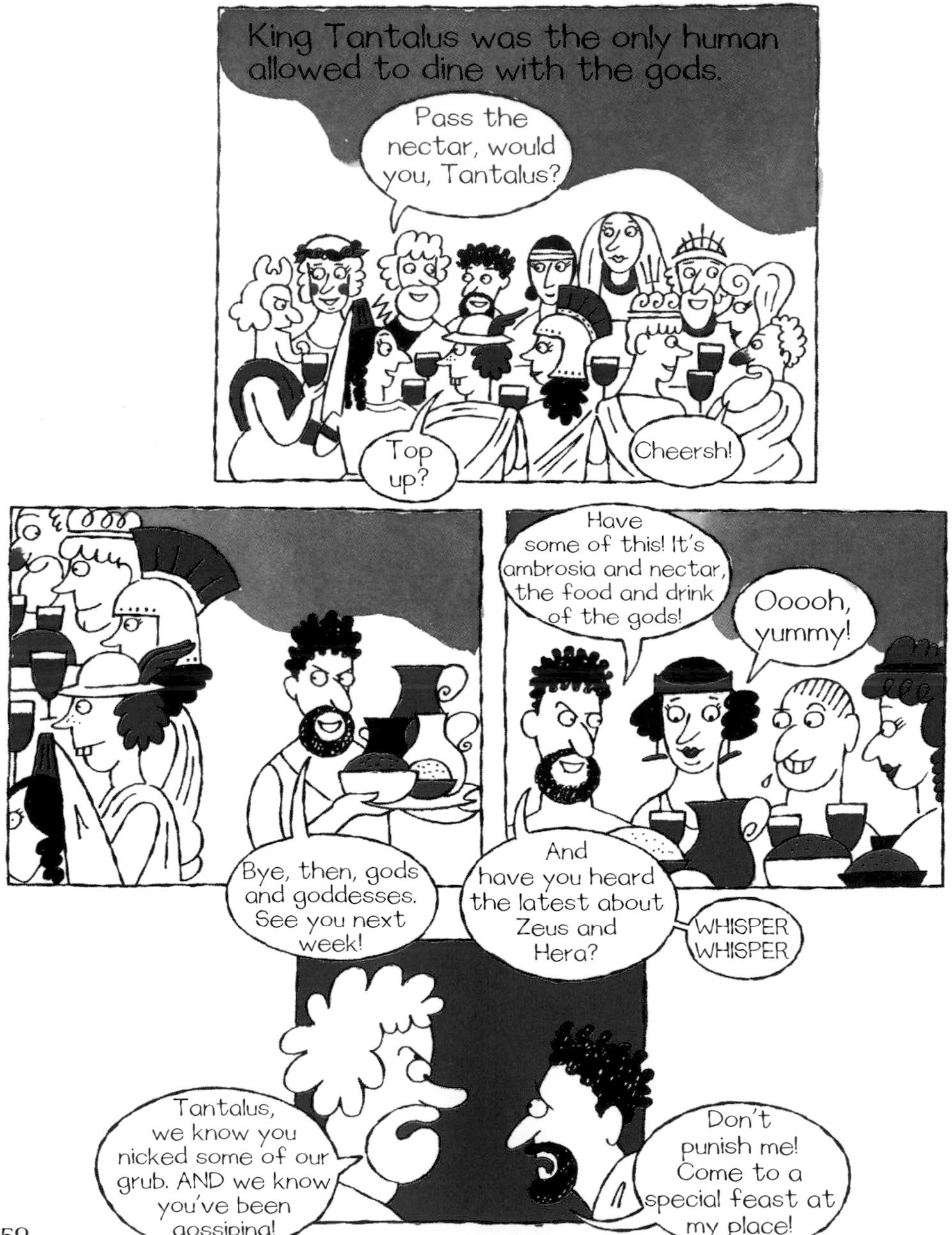

Bye, then, gods and goddesses. See you next week!

Have some of this! It's ambrosia and nectar, the food and drink of the gods!

Ooooh, yummy!

And have you heard the latest about Zeus and Hera?

WHISPER WHISPER

Tantalus, we know you nicked some of our grub. AND we know you've been gossiping!

Don't punish me! Come to a special feast at my place!

They sent Tantalus to the Underworld. There he stood up to his neck in water that shrank away when he tried to drink it, and surrounded by fruit trees just out of his reach.

KING OEDIPUS

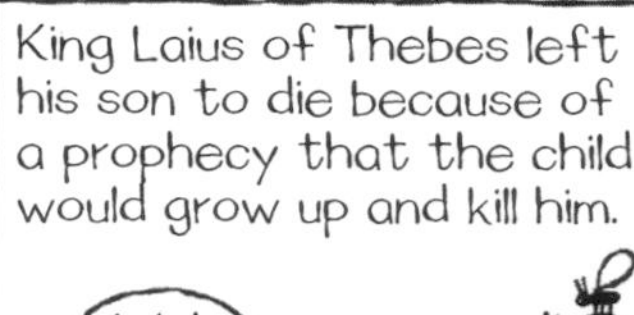

Years later, Oedipus was walking to Thebes, when . . .

Then his day got even worse . . .

I am the Sphinx and I've a riddle for you. If you don't get it right, I'll throttle you!

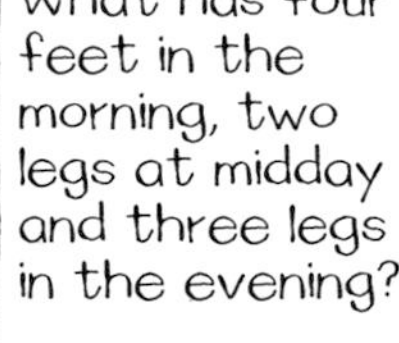

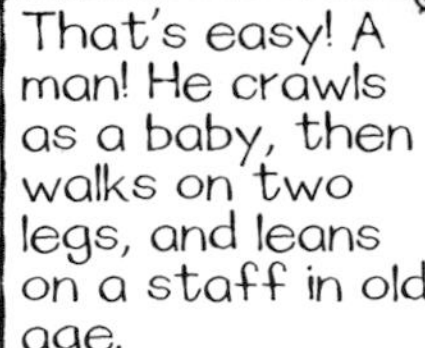
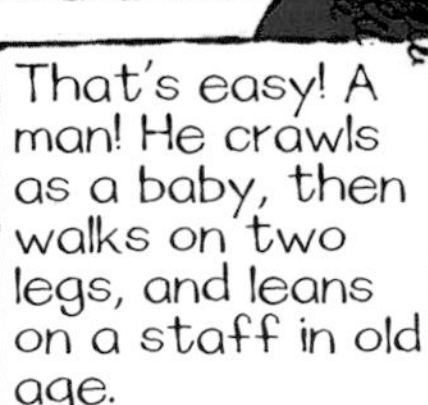

As his prize for getting rid of the Sphinx, Oedipus was made king of Thebes.
I'm Queen Jocasta.
My husband died recently. I'll marry you instead!
All was well until one day a prophet arrived at the palace.
Oedipus! You have killed your father and married your mother!
Nonsense! My father's a shepherd, I haven't seen my mother in ages, and I haven't killed anyone!
Oh, apart from that traveller on the way to Thebes!
The shepherd isn't your father. He found you on a hillside.
Oh no! The traveller you killed was my husband. And YOU are the baby we abandoned!
!!!!!
I'm off to wander the world as a lonely, blind beggar.
We're the Furies, fearsome goddesses who avenge unpunished crimes.
And we're going to follow you!

HELEN OF TROY
I'm Eris, goddess of strife.
And if there's one thing I can't stand, it's not being invited to big, posh weddings!
GNASH
Love the hat!
Oh, dahling, thank you.
So Eris sent a golden apple to the wedding feast.
For the Fairest
It's mine!
A mortal man shall judge whether Hera, Athene or Aphrodite is the most beautiful . . .
I appoint you, Paris, Prince of Troy!
Thanks a lot, Zeus.

Pick me, Hera, queen of the gods, and I'll make you a powerful king!
Choose me, Athene, warrior goddess, and I promise you'll win any battle you fight!
Choose me, Aphrodite, goddess of love, and I'll give you the most beautiful woman in the world!
It's a difficult decision, but . . . Aphrodite, you're the fairest!
simper simper
Aphrodite had forgotten to mention that the world's most beautiful woman, Helen, was already married to someone else.
Yes! To me, King Menelaus of Sparta. After he'd chosen Aphrodite, Paris came and stole Helen from me.
Grrr
And I'm really cross about it!
I'm Helen of Troy now. But Menelaus is very cross indeed . . .

THE TROJAN WAR BEGINS

The Greeks besieged the city of Troy for ten years.

ACHILLES' HEEL

Achilles became the best Greek warrior fighting in the Trojan War.
Haarrgghh! Take that, Trojans!
Urk
Great god Apollo, you're on the Trojans' side. Can't you help?
I'm fed up with that Achilles. He's killing all the Trojan soldiers and he never seems to get hurt.
Yes, he's getting on my nerves too. Fire an arrow at him and I'll help you.
Hoh heh!
Urk
Oh no! What are we going to do without mighty Achilles?
Hmmm . . . I'm Odysseus and I've got an idea . . .

The Greek warrior Odysseus had a cunning plan . . .

Because the Trojans think the horse is a gift for Athene, they bring it inside the city.

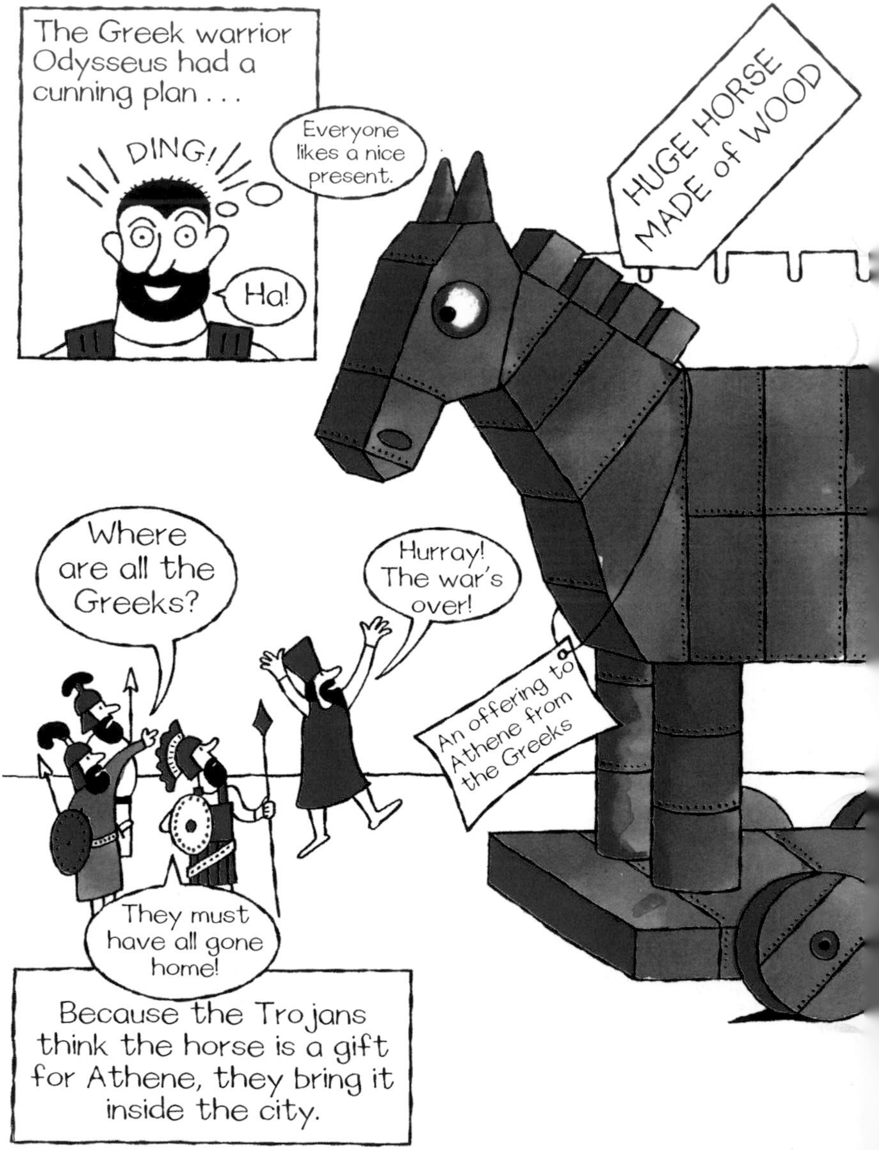

Good grief!
What a lovely present!
Greek soldiers hidden in here
Move up a bit!
Ow!
That's my foot!
Shhh!
Odysseus's plan worked: the Greek warriors came out of the horse in the dead of night, sacked the city of Troy and won the war.
BIFF
Nng!
Urk
BASH
Urk
Hooray!
We're the best!

THE MURDER OF AGAMEMNON

Orestes was Agamemnon and Clytemnestra's son.
I have to avenge my father's death. I've been away from the family for so long that Aegisthus and my mother won't recognise me . . .
Gah!
Urk
Urk
We're after you, Orestes!
Woo!!!
Boo!!!
You can't get away with killing your own mother!
Nng
Argh
The Furies are driving me mad!
We need to sort this out. Orestes, you'll be put on trial . . .
Of course, great goddess Athene.
What could be worse than being chased by those scary Furies?
And I will be judge. Well, I am goddess of wisdom. Orestes can go free!
Boo!
Curses!
Phew!

THE VOYAGES OF ODYSSEUS

Baa!
Gaaaa! Sheep-rustlers!
Erg!
YUM!
Urk
SHARPENED TREE TRUNK
Uhh?
Aargh!
That was a close one!
Here, Odysseus! A bag of winds for you.
Oh, it's Aeolus, god of the winds. Thanks!
But open it carefully to release one wind at a time, won't you?

What do you reckon's in that sack?
Let's open it!
Yeah!
WHOOOSH!
Perhaps we shouldn't have done that!
The winds blew Odysseus's ships to a land of cannibals.
Heh heh! We've eaten the crew and destroyed nearly all the ships!
Odysseus escaped and sailed to an island ruled by Circe the witch.
Where I turned most of Odysseus's crew into pigs. Tee hee!
Oink
Oink oink
Odysseus, let me help you get back your crew.
Thanks, Hermes, messenger god!
This special flower will protect you from Circe's magic.
. . . And now I want my crew turned back into men.
Oh, all right.
Oink, ooh, thank goodness!

Odysseus, before you can get home you must journey to the Underworld.
Who'd have thought that sailing from Troy to Ithaca would be this difficult?
But in the Underworld the ghosts gave him some useful tips . . .
Make a sacrifice to Poseidon and you'll live to old age.
Whatever you do, DON'T eat the Cattle of the Sun!
There's trouble in Ithaca!
Thanks for the advice, everyone!
Wooo!
Back on Circe's island . . .
I have some advice, too. Not far from here, the Sirens' song will lure you to your deaths if you hear it.
Plug your ears with beeswax! Now, farewell!
Bye, Circe, and thanks. No hard feelings about the pigs.
Tra la la
Can't hear a thing.
I wanted to hear the Sirens' song so I'm tied to the mast to stop me going to them.

Odysseus sailed on until he came to a narrow pass. On one side was Scylla.
slaver slaver
I eat sailors.
On the other side was Charybdis.
I create a perilous whirlpool.
BURP
Eek!
Urk
Bellow
Phew. We made it to the Island of the Sun.
Remember, crew, don't eat the cattle!
We've been here ages. I'm starving.
Just one little cow won't hurt . . .
YUM!
As punishment for eating the Cattle of the Sun, Zeus wrecked Odysseus's ship and drowned the crew.
I'm the only survivor.

Eventually Odysseus washed up on an island where the nymph Calypso lived.
I'm in love!
swoon swoon
Come on, Calypso. You've kept me here for seven years – please let me go home now!
I've been ordered by the gods, so I suppose I'll have to let you go.
Here, I'll help you build a raft.
Not again!
Luckily I was helped by the Phaeacians, who gave me this ship to sail home in.
Finally, Odysseus made it to Ithaca where he was welcomed by his faithful wife, Penelope, and their son, Telemachus.
And, after getting rid of Penelope's pesky suitors . . .
And making a sacrifice to Poseidon . . .
That was the 'trouble' the ghost warned him about . . .
We all lived happily ever after!

The Greeks and Romans (and everyone else)

It's because of us that Neptune, Jupiter, Venus and Mars are in the solar system!

But mostly it's because of us, the Greeks!

Ha!

After the Romans, people kept on telling Greek myths.

Including me, the Great Bard, Shakespeare.

Tracey Turner

Tracey Turner writes books for children and adults about lots of different subjects, including famous writers, rude words, mysterious sliding rocks and, of course, the entire history of the Universe. She lives in Bath with Tom and their son, Toby. If she could have a divine attibute, she thinks casting thunderbolts and lightning might be fun.

Sally Kindberg

Sally Kindberg is an illustrator and writer. She once went to Elf School in Iceland, has writton a book about hair, sailed on a tall ship to Lisbon and drawn the complete history of the world and the Universe. When not drawing she enjoys interviewing people and writing about them. She has a daughter called Emerald and lives in London with 84 robots.

And for more Comic Strip genius, don't miss . . .

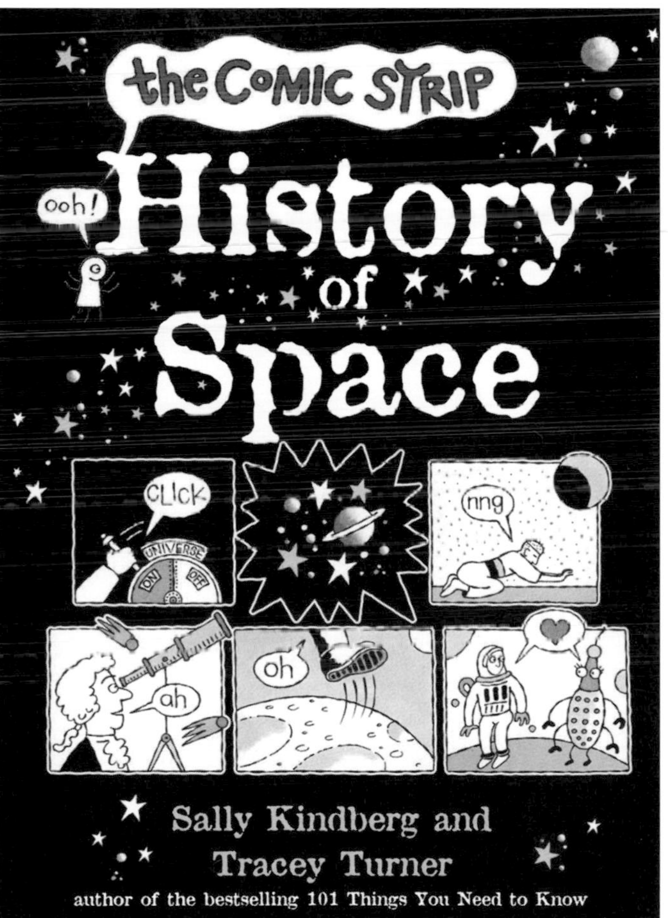
the COMIC STRIP
ooh!
History of Space
CLICK
UNIVERSE
ON
OFF
nng
ah
oh
Sally Kindberg and
Tracey Turner
author of the bestselling 101 Things You Need to Know